The Nkosi Family

Written by
Elda Lyster

Illustrated by
Jeff Rankin

NEW READERS PROJECT

THE NEW READERS PROJECT

The New Readers Project of the Department of Adult and Community Education, University of Natal, Durban develops and supports adult literacy and basic English Second Language skills by producing books in simple language for the entertainment and education of adults. Each of the books has been evaluated and modified by potential readers.

The project was set up with funding from the Canadian Embassy; The Chairman's Fund Educational Trust; Development and Peace; The Hexagon Trust; The Energos Foundation; Rockefeller Brothers Fund and the Trust for Educational Advancement in South Africa.

Thanks

We thank the following people for their help in evaluating this book:

Ephraim Chiliza, Joseph Luthuli, Jack Mbuyisa, Hamilton Mkhize, Joseph Mlangeni, Ndukuzempi Neni, Samuel Ngwazi and Michael Banda of the Spar Natal Zulu Literacy Class;

Gertrude Khanyile, Johannes Khanyile, Bongani Mngadi, Clement Vezi and Abie Shangase of the Spar Natal English Group;

Esther Dlamini, Mathami Mgwaba, Egnes Mjoka, Mantombi Mthembu, Thoko Myende, Amy Ndlovu, Desmond Ndlovu, Joseph Ngidi, Nonhlanhla Ngidi, Cecilia Ntombela and Bongani Shabane of the Vulingqondo Adult Centre;

Nozipho Dlamini, Bhekuyise Dlomo, Leonard Gamede, Sonosakhe Gazu, Antony Gebela, Fikelephi Khuzwayo, Bukhosi Lushaba, Mandle Ngubane, Jabulani Mthokozani Mgijima, Maureen Niniza Mbhele, Joyce Sithole, Nomdanti Zuma, Aleck Zungu, Buyisile Mthembu and Joseph Sishi of the Spoornet English Literacy Group;

Beatrice Mabaso, Zanele Mabaso and Rosa Lyster.

How to contact us

If you want to know more about the New Readers Project or find out about other books which we publish, please contact:

Department of Adult and Community Education
University of Natal
Durban
4041
South Africa

This is a story about the Nkosi family.
It tells you about them.

What do they like?
What do they want?
What do they feel?
What do they dream?

The Nkosi family lives in a house in
Inanda.
There are seven people in the family.

Bonga Nkosi, the
father, works as a
packer in a factory.

MaDube Nkosi,
the mother, sells
food at the station.

Gogo Nkosi looks after
the small children at
home.

Saneliso Nkosi, the first-born, is looking for a job.

Mbali Nkosi, the daughter, is in standard nine.

Sipho Nkosi, the second son, is in standard two.

Philile Nkosi is two years old and is the daughter of Mbali.

3

What do they like?

Nkosi likes beer and horse-racing.

MaDube likes peace and quiet.

Gogo Nkosi likes the radio and
knitting.

Saneliso likes going to meetings
and girls.

Mbali likes Lucky Dube and
reading.

Sipho likes soccer.

Philile likes porridge.

What do they want?

"I just want some spare cash," says
Nkosi.

"I need a new hat for church," says
MaDube.

14

"An old lady needs a warm
blanket," says Gogo.

"Please give me some money for shoes," says Saneliso.

"I really want my hair done," says
Mbali.

"Please give me some money for a football," says Sipho.

18

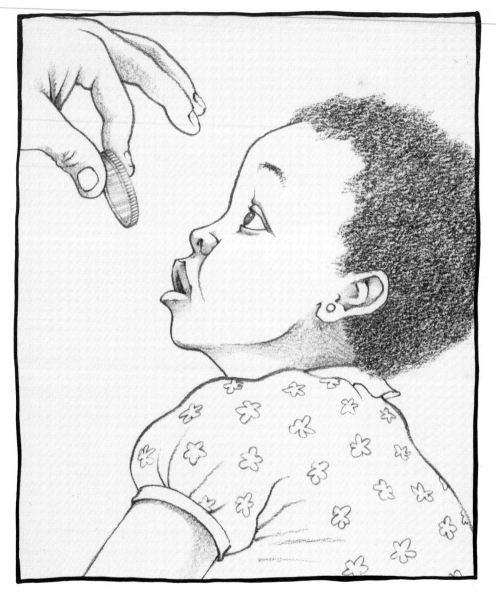

"What's money?" says Philile.

How do they feel?

Nkosi feels worried.

MaDube feels crazy.

Gogo feels peaceful.

Saneliso feels bored.

Mbali feels happy.

Sipho feels sad.

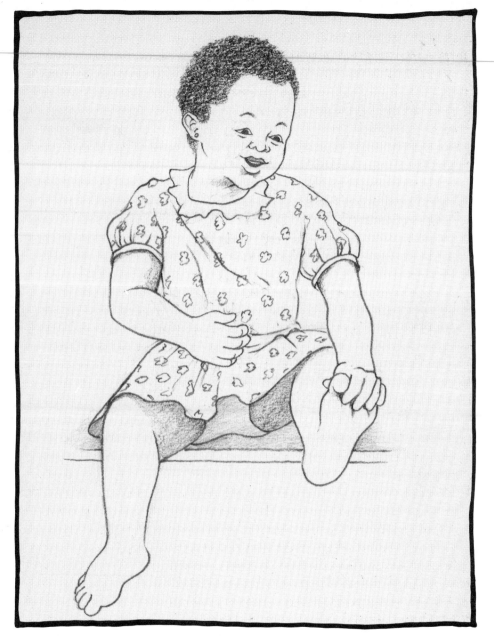

Philile feels her toes.

What are their dreams?

"Let's dream," says MaDube.

"I'm the owner of a new house,"
says Nkosi.

"I'm resting for a week," says
MaDube.

"I'm young and strong," says Gogo.

"I'm a T.V. presenter," says Saneliso.

"I'm dancing with Lucky Dube,"
says Mbali.

"I'm Jomo Sono," says Sipho.

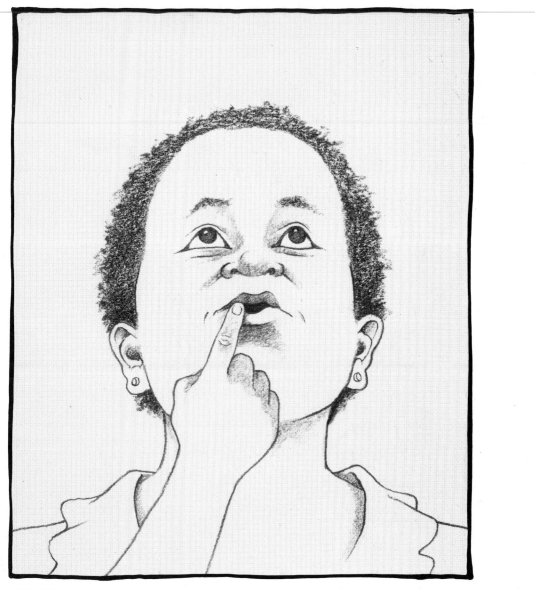

"What's a dream?" says Philile.